SCHOLASTIC

ACTIVE English Workbook 7

Name: ______________________________

Class: ______________________________

First edition: 2012
Reprinted: 2012, 2014 (twice), 2015, 2016, 2017, 2018, 2019, 2020, 2023

ISBN-978-81-8477-735-2

Preface

The creators of ACTIVE English believe that literacy acquisition is dependent on the integrated teaching of reading, writing, listening and speaking skills, and the engagement of learners. This integrated approach to learning and literacy development is advocated through a systematic and consistent instructional design and scope and sequence.

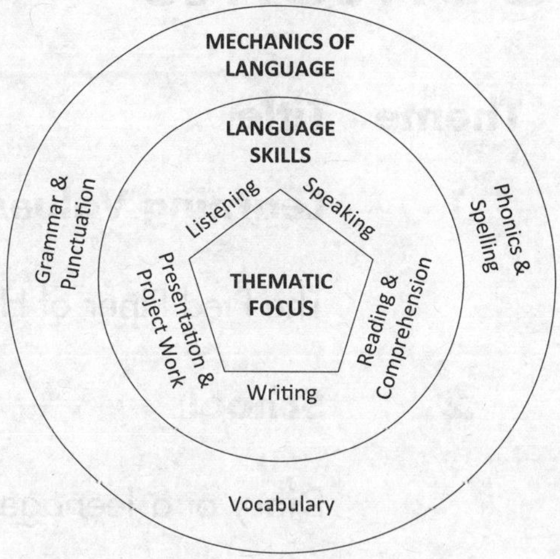

This Workbook can be used to extend the learning in the Coursebook or as an independent learning resource.

Coursebook Correlation to Extend Learning

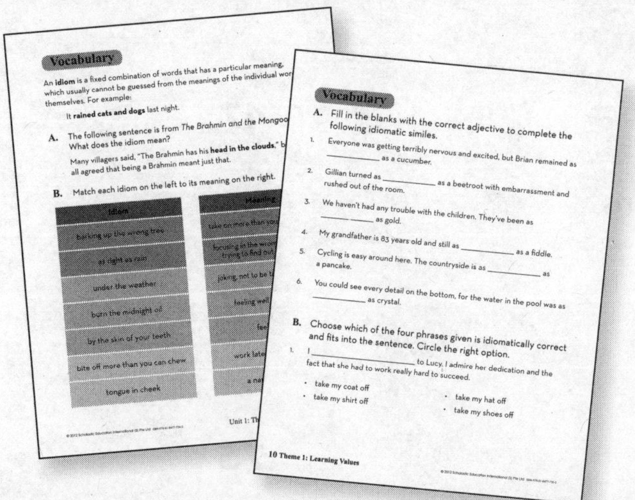

Vocabulary

An **idiom** is a fixed combination of words that has a particular meaning, which usually cannot be guessed from the meanings of the individual words themselves. For example:

It **rained cats and dogs** last night.

A. The following sentence is from *The Brahmin and the Mongoose*. What does the idiom mean?

Many villagers said, "The Brahmin has his **head in the clouds**," but all agreed that being a Brahmin meant just that.

B. Match each idiom on the left to its meaning on the right.

Idiom
barking up the wrong tree
as right as rain
under the weather
burn the midnight oil
by the skin of your teeth
bite off more than you can chew
tongue in cheek

Vocabulary

A. Fill in the blanks with the correct adjective to complete the following idiomatic similes.

1. Everyone was getting terribly nervous and excited, but Brian remained as ________ as a cucumber.
2. Gillian turned as ________ as a beetroot with embarrassment and rushed out of the room.
3. We haven't had any trouble with the children. They've been as ________ as gold.
4. My grandfather is 83 years old and still as ________ as a fiddle.
5. Cycling is easy around here. The countryside is as ________ as a pancake.
6. You could see every detail on the bottom, for the water in the pool was as ________ as crystal.

B. Choose which of the four phrases given is idiomatically correct and fits into the sentence. Circle the right option.

1. I ________ to Lucy. I admire her dedication and the fact that she had to work really hard to succeed.
- take my coat off
- take my shirt off
- take my hat off
- take my shoes off

10 Theme 1: Learning Values

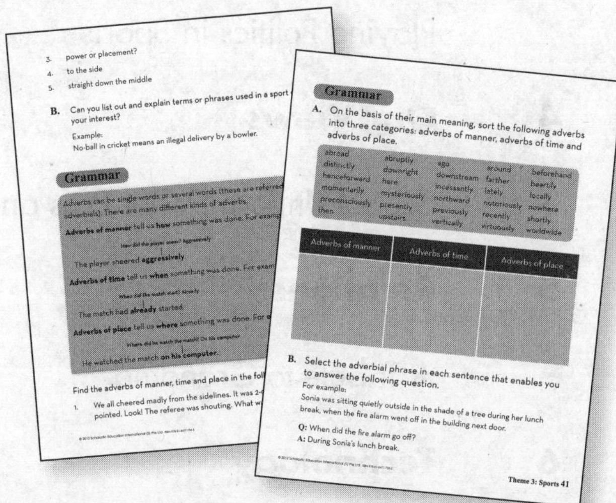

3. power or placement?
4. to the side
5. straight down the middle

B. Can you list out and explain terms or phrases used in a sport of your interest?

Example:
No-ball in cricket means an illegal delivery by a bowler.

Grammar

Adverbs can be single words or several words (these are referred to as adverbials). There are many different kinds of adverbs.

Adverbs of manner tell us **how** something was done.

The player sneered **aggressively**.

Adverbs of time tell us **when** something was done.

The match had **already** started.

Adverbs of place tell us **where** something was done.

He watched the match **on his computer**.

Find the adverbs of manner, time and place in the following...

1. We all cheered madly from the sidelines. It was 2-... pointed. Look! The referee was shouting. What w...

Grammar

A. On the basis of their main meaning, sort the following adverbs into three categories: adverbs of manner, adverbs of time and adverbs of place.

abroad, abruptly, ago, around, beforehand, distinctly, downright, downstream, farther, heartily, henceforward, here, incessantly, lately, locally, momentarily, mysteriously, northward, notoriously, nowhere, preconsciously, pleasantly, previously, recently, shortly, then, upstairs, vertically, virtuously, worldwide

Adverbs of manner	Adverbs of time	Adverbs of place

B. Select the adverbial phrase in each sentence that enables you to answer the following question.

For example:
Sonia was sitting quietly outside in the shade of a tree during her lunch break, when the fire alarm went off in the building next door.

Q: When did the fire alarm go off?
A: During Sonia's lunch break.

Theme 3: Sports 41

Each theme in the Workbook correlates to a theme in the Coursebook in terms of its topic and language skills. The exercises provide additional practice for reinforcement and consolidation.

Authentic and Varied Text Types

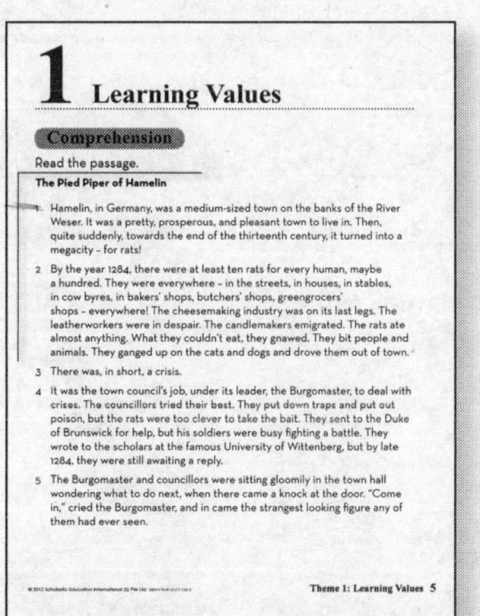

1 Learning Values

Comprehension

Read the passage.

The Pied Piper of Hamelin

1 Hamelin, in Germany, was a medium-sized town on the banks of the River Weser. It was a pretty, prosperous, and pleasant town to live in. Then, quite suddenly, towards the end of the thirteenth century, it turned into a megacity – for rats!

2 By the year 1284, there were at least ten rats for every human, maybe a hundred. They were everywhere – in the streets, in houses, in stables, in cow byres, in bakers' shops, butchers' shops, greengrocers' shops – everywhere! The cheesemaking industry was on its last legs. The leatherworkers were in despair. The candlemakers emigrated. The rats ate almost anything. What they couldn't eat, they gnawed. They bit people and animals. They ganged up on the cats and dogs and drove them out of town.

3 There was, in short, a crisis.

4 It was the town council's job, under its leader, the Burgomaster, to deal with crises. The councillors tried their best. They put down traps and put out poison, but the rats were too clever to take the bait. They sent to the Duke of Brunswick for help, but his soldiers were busy fighting a battle. They wrote to the scholars at the famous University of Wittenberg, but by late 1284, they were still awaiting a reply.

5 The Burgomaster and councillors were sitting gloomily in the town hall wondering what to do next, when there came a knock at the door. "Come in," cried the Burgomaster, and in came the strangest looking figure any of them had ever seen.

Theme 1: Learning Values 5

Authentic texts in a variety of text types engage students and prepare them for language in the real world.

Integration of Language Skills

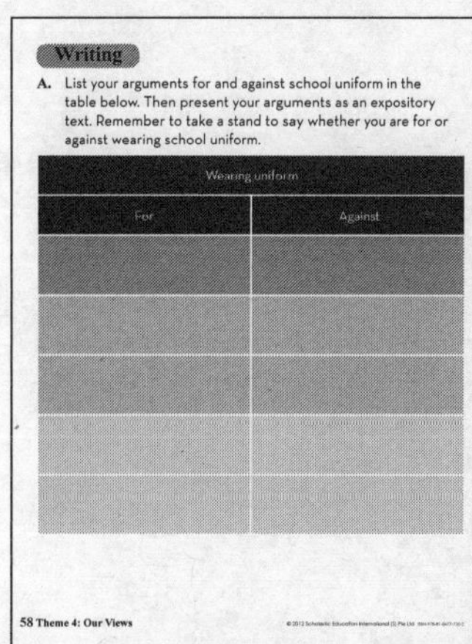

Writing

A. List your arguments for and against school uniform in the table below. Then present your arguments as an expository text. Remember to take a stand to say whether you are for or against wearing school uniform.

Wearing uniform	
For	Against

58 Theme 4: Our Views

The writing exercises in each unit consolidate the language skills covered in the Coursebook and provide extension activities for the comprehension passage.

 ISBN-978-81-8477-735-2

Contents

 ISBN-978-81-8477-735-2

1 Learning Values

Comprehension

Read the passage.

The Pied Piper of Hamelin

1 Hamelin, in Germany, was a medium-sized town on the banks of the River Weser. It was a pretty, prosperous, and pleasant town to live in. Then, quite suddenly, towards the end of the thirteenth century, it turned into a megacity – for rats!

2 By the year 1284, there were at least ten rats for every human, maybe a hundred. They were everywhere – in the streets, in houses, in stables, in cow byres, in bakers' shops, butchers' shops, greengrocers' shops – everywhere! The cheesemaking industry was on its last legs. The leatherworkers were in despair. The candlemakers emigrated. The rats ate almost anything. What they couldn't eat, they gnawed. They bit people and animals. They ganged up on the cats and dogs and drove them out of town.

3 There was, in short, a crisis.

4 It was the town council's job, under its leader, the Burgomaster, to deal with crises. The councillors tried their best. They put down traps and put out poison, but the rats were too clever to take the bait. They sent to the Duke of Brunswick for help, but his soldiers were busy fighting a battle. They wrote to the scholars at the famous University of Wittenberg, but by late 1284, they were still awaiting a reply.

5 The Burgomaster and councillors were sitting gloomily in the town hall wondering what to do next, when there came a knock at the door. "Come in," cried the Burgomaster, and in came the strangest looking figure any of them had ever seen.

 ISBN-978-81-8477-735-2

6 It wasn't so much his tallness, his thinness, his long blond hair, short blond beard or piercing blue eyes that were strange. It was his clothes. His jacket, hose, hat and cloak were of every colour under the sun, with red and yellow predominating.

7 "Let me introduce myself," he said. "I am the Pied Piper. You have a rat problem, I believe. Give me a thousand guilders and I'll rid your town of rats!"

8 "A thousand!" exclaimed the Burgomaster. "We'll give you fifty! Can you do it?"

9 "My references!" replied the Pied Piper, producing a scroll. "The Sultan of Baghdad's kitchens are cockroach-free, thanks to me. I trust one of you knows Arabic? Promise me my thousand guilders and I will set to at once, for I am rather pressed for time."

10 "Of course," said the Burgomaster, and the many-coloured musician stepped out into the street and put a small wooden pipe to his lips.

11 What he blew seemed tuneless to humans, but to rats it was a spell-binding melody. Waking, sleeping, gnawing, nibbling, they left whatever they were doing and came out to follow it. A river of rats flowed down the main street at the heels of the Piper until it reached the banks of the Weser and poured itself in.

12 "The rats are all dead, drowned in the river," said the Pied Piper returning to the Town Hall.

13 "That'll be one thousand guilders, if you please."

14 "Have they really gone?" asked the Burgomaster.

15 "Every single one," returned the Piper. "One thousand ..."

16 "Just a moment!"

17 The Burgomaster and councillors conferred in whispers.

18 "Perhaps we were rather rash," suggested one councillor.

19 "Think what we could do with a thousand guilders!" put in another.

20 "Offer him fifty," said the Deputy Burgomaster. "Dead rats don't bite!" He tapped his nose significantly.

 ISBN-978-81-8477-735-2

21 “My good man,” said the Burgomaster. “We should like to offer you the sincerest thanks of the citizens of Hamelin, and this purse of fifty guilders.”

22 “Fifty?” protested the Piper. “You promised me one thousand.”

23 “I did say fifty,” said the Burgomaster. “It’s our final offer. Take it or leave it.”

24 Without another word, the Piper turned his back on the Burgomaster, went out into the streets and started to play again.

25 This time his tune was anything but unattractive to humans, except for little children. From home, school, everywhere, the children of Hamelin poured into the streets and followed the Piper, just like the rats. The townspeople watched in horror as their children skipped off towards the river. But at the last moment, the Pied Piper turned aside and, instead, led them up a steep hill outside the town.

26 “The hill is very steep,” thought the citizens. “Soon they will get tired and stop.” But at that moment, a large cave opened up in the side of the hill. In went the Piper, in went all the children and the cave mouth shut tight.

27 None of the children who went in were ever seen again in Hamelin. But one little boy was left. He was lame and unable to skip as fast as his playmates. When the cave closed, he was left outside.

28 The boy told the grieving townspeople that the Piper’s music was irresistibly sweet. It conjured up visions of a perfect land where it was always summer, the flowers bloomed all year, nobody was ever hungry and nobody cried. He was sure his playmates had gone there. He felt sad and lonely to be left behind.

29 On the other side of Europe, in the country of Romania, there once were people who looked like Germans, spoke German, and were altogether German in their ways. It was said that they emerged one day from a cave in the mountainside above the valley where they lived.

30 But that, perhaps, is only a story.

 ISBN-978-81-8477-735-2

A. Answer the following questions.

Level 1

1. Where and when is this tale set?

2. What makes the Pied Piper appear strange?

3. How much does the Burgomaster promise to pay the Pied Piper?

4. What happens to the children of Hamelin?

Level 2

5. Is magic an important element in this story? Give reason for your answer.

6. How would you describe the Pied Piper's physical appearance and his character? For example, you can note, if he is a kind person or not.

 ISBN-978-81-8477-735-2

7. Is the Burgomaster telling the truth when he says, "I did say fifty"?

____

____

8. How would you describe the attitude of the Burgomaster and the councillors towards the Pied Piper after he killed all the rats?

____

____

9. Do you think that this story has a moral? If so, what is its moral?

____

____

Level 3

10. Write a word or a short phrase to explain the meaning of the following words as they are used in the passage.

    a. megacity ____________________ (paragraph 1)

    b. on its last legs ____________________ (paragraph 2)

    c. ganged up on ____________________ (paragraph 2)

    d. under the sun ____________________ (paragraph 6)

    e. spell-binding ____________________ (paragraph 11)

 ISBN-978-81-8477-735-2

Vocabulary

A. Fill in the blanks with the correct adjective to complete the following idiomatic similes.

1. Everyone was getting terribly nervous and excited, but Brian remained as ______________ as a cucumber.

2. Gillian turned as ______________ as a beetroot with embarrassment and rushed out of the room.

3. We haven't had any trouble with the children. They've been as ______________ as gold.

4. My grandfather is 83 years old and still as ______________ as a fiddle.

5. Cycling is easy around here. The countryside is as ______________ as a pancake.

6. You could see every detail on the bottom, for the water in the pool was as ______________ as crystal.

B. Choose which of the four phrases given is idiomatically correct and fits into the sentence. Circle the right option.

1. I ______________________ to Lucy. I admire her dedication and the fact that she had to work really hard to succeed.

   - take my coat off
   - take my hat off
   - take my shirt off
   - take my shoes off

 ISBN-978-81-8477-735-2

2. The airline didn't tell us anything. They left us completely ____________________ about what was happening.

- in the dark
- in the fog
- in the night
- in the shadow

3. Are you ____________________? You'd be crazy to take such a risk!

- out of your brain
- out of your head
- out of your mind
- out of your sanity

4. I can't stand that dreadful noise a moment longer. It's driving me completely ____________________.

- up the garden path
- up the rope
- up the stairs
- up the wall

5. We were trying to keep the date a secret, but Tom ____________________.

- let the cat out of the bag
- let the cow out of the field
- let the horse out of the stable
- let the tiger out of his cage

 ISBN-978-81-8477-735-2

C. From the four adjectives in the right-hand column, circle the one that most precisely expresses the opposite meaning to the main meaning of the adjective in the left-hand column.

Word	Adjectives			
1. scarce	rich	plentiful	frequent	crowded
2. rough	comfortable	delicate	slippery	smooth
3. pliable	straight	rigid	immobile	flat
4. nervous	calm	cheerful	intense	pacific
5. ignorant	intelligent	knowing	stupid	knowledgeable
6. harmonious	discordant	hostile	noisy	unpleasant

D. Sort the adjectives in the box into contrasting pairs (that is, pairs with opposite meanings, such as **easy** and **difficult** or **extravagant** and **frugal**). Write the contrasting pairs in the lines below.

stingy	foolish	generous	glum	enthusiastic
repulsive	bright	plain	peculiar	patterned
sensitive	ordinary	wise	attractive	outgoing
cheerful	shy	inconsiderate	half-hearted	dim

_______________ _______________

_______________ _______________

 ISBN-978-81-8477-735-2

E. Fill in each blank in the passage with a suitable adjective from the box.

bleached	fragrant	scarce	intense	oppressive
shady	refreshing	gloomy	crowded	

What a contrast! Soraya emerged from the ______________ passageway into sunlight so ______________ that she had to shut her eyes. Cautiously she reopened them, raising her hand to shield them from the glare. Everything in the street had a ______________ appearance, as if in time the sunlight would reduce all colours to white.

 ISBN-978-81-8477-735-2

There was hardly anybody about. Soraya barely recognised it as the ______________ thoroughfare she had walked through the previous evening. Customers were ______________ at this time of day. Most of the businesses were closed during the hours of ______________ heat. Suddenly, a small man in white darted out of one doorway, crossed the street and disappeared into another. Soraya decided to follow him.

She pushed aside a bead curtain, walked down a short corridor and came out in a ______________ courtyard, with a great spreading tree at its centre, the ______________ sound of a small fountain and the ______________ aroma of fresh coffee.

Grammar

A. Are these sentences declarative or interrogative? Add correct punctuation mark at the end of each sentence.

1. There are several horses in the field, but no cows
2. Where the Pied Piper came from, nobody could say
3. How many rats were there for every man, woman and child
4. Did you see the man in the strange red and yellow hat
5. Tomorrow I will give you my answer.
6. Should I wear my red and yellow dress or my blue and white one

 ISBN-978-81-8477-735-2

B. Change the following declarative sentences into interrogative sentences.

For example:

The boy speaks English. → Does the boy speak English?

1. Harry has had a phone call from Australia.

____

2. Shanti wanted to go with the others.

____

3. She has a copy of the book.

____

4. The dog sleeps in a basket by the fire.

____

5. They will be at the station by nine o'clock.

____

C. Which of these sentences are compound sentences and which are complex sentences? Write **Cd** (for compound sentence) or **Cx** (for complex sentence) in the brackets.

1. The weather was fine and sunny last week, but this week it has rained almost every day. (   )

2. I don't like football and I absolutely loathe badminton. (   )

 ISBN-978-81-8477-735-2

3. Before he signed the document, Mr Chatterjee read it through once again very carefully. ( )

4. Would you like to tell Peter or shall I tell him? ( )

5. I had to fetch Sandra home from school because she complained of feeling ill. ( )

6. Brian still doesn't know when the exam is going to be held. ( )

D. Underline the subject and the verb in the main clauses of the following sentences.

1. Hamelin is a town in northern central Germany that lies on the banks of the River Weser.

2. Can you tell me where I can find Hamelin on the map?

3. If Roger brings the sandwiches, we will bring the drinks.

4. The dog that bit Sarah actually belonged to her teacher.

5. I can't remember what I was supposed to say to you.

6. Simon, whom you've met before, will meet you at the entrance.

 ISBN-978-81-8477-735-2

Writing

A. Imagine you are the little boy who was left outside the cave. Write a paragraph about how you felt after you were left behind. Use the information from the text to help you.

B. Imagine you are the Burgomaster. Write a diary entry about your thoughts and feelings about the Pied Piper. Your diary entry should cover the following points:

1. Your impression of the Pied Piper at different stages of the story.
2. Whether you think you are responsible for the loss of the children.

 ISBN-978-81-8477-735-2

2 School

Comprehension

Read the passage.

Diary of a Teenage Girl

Monday

1 School was the pits today! First I got a detention for being late. It wasn't my fault – the bus was late – but Ms Black was in a foul mood and wouldn't listen to anything I said. They're letting me do the detention tomorrow. I can't do it this afternoon because of my stupid music lesson. I'm never going to be any good at the piano but Mum says I must "persevere".

2 Then – disaster! – we got a surprise test on the English novel we're supposed to read at home this term. I had chosen *Wuthering Heights* – I had seen an old film about it and it seemed really romantic – but I haven't actually got round to reading it yet. I mean, we've got until the end of term to finish it – and that's yonks away! Ms Jackson said that we were told to read a bit everyday and not leave it all till the last minute. I wrote down what I could remember of the film but that wasn't much! Of course, Jenny Smith had finished hers and knew all about it. I hate her!

3 I've got loads of homework. No time to go round and see Jane or even to watch the telly. I wish I didn't have to go to school. It's a real bore!

Tuesday

4 Another bad hair day! How could I have two such awful days in a row? We got the English test back in the first period and I came bottom of the class. I got the *Wuthering Heights* film mixed up with some other old film – *Jane Eyre* or something – and Ms Jackson was absolutely furious. I've to read the whole thing by next week and write an essay on it. It's just not fair! Nobody else has to do that.

 ISBN-978-81-8477-735-2

5 I can't believe it, but I've got another detention! That's two this week and it's only Tuesday! I only hope my father doesn't find out or he'll go bananas. He's always going on about the importance of a good education. The detention's for forgetting my French homework. Mum gave me a lift to school this morning and I must have left it in the car.

6 I was the only person in detention and it was so boring! I had to write an essay called *The Importance of Punctuality*. I really couldn't think of much to say and so I'll probably get another detention for that.

7 I better get on with *Wuthering Heights.*

Wednesday

8 Hurrah! I got through the whole day without a detention – and without even a word of criticism. I must be becoming a model pupil!

9 Things got even better after school. When I got to detention, who was there but the hunk who's just started in the year above me! The others will be so jealous. Everyone fancies him like mad! He's new to the area as well as to the school and I casually offered to show him around. He said that was cool and we've made a date for Saturday. Wicked! I can't wait! I wonder if Mum'll buy me a new outfit. I've got absolutely nothing decent to wear.

10 My luck just ran out! Mum says I've got enough clothes to open my own shop and I'm certainly not getting anything new. She says that they're all very nice, but what does she know? I'd borrow something from Jane, but I don't want her to know yet about the date with the hunk – he's called Dave and I can't wait to see him again!

Thursday

11 It's just not my week! I've got a huge zit on my chin. It'll never disappear by Saturday. Mum says it's so small that she can hardly see it, but she's just trying to cheer me up. I bought some stuff from the chemist at lunchtime. I just hope it works. I can't help looking at the zit in the mirror and it's depressing me.

 ISBN-978-81-8477-735-2

Friday

12 The perfect end to the perfect week! The zit isn't any better and Dad met Ms Jackson and she told him about my detentions. She's so mean! Dad gave me the usual lecture about pulling up my socks and appreciating the value of a good education. He went on and on, but at least, he didn't give out any punishment. I apologised and promised to do better. I was terrified that I would be grounded and I would have to cancel my date with Dave, but everything's all right now. I can't wait for tomorrow!

A. Answer the following questions.

Level 1

1. Briefly mention the three things that occurred on Monday to make it "the pits" for the writer.

___

___

2. How did the writer perform in the surprise test and what was the cause behind it?

___

___

3. What happened at the first detention?

___

___

 ISBN-978-81-8477-735-2

4. What "stuff" did the writer buy from the chemist?

5. How did the girl respond to her father's lecture? Explain her behaviour.

Level 2

6. Give a possible explanation for the writer's hatred for Jenny Smith.

7. Explain why the second detention turned out to be better than expected.

8. Comment on the writer's use of the word "perfect" to describe the way things turned out for her.

 ISBN-978-81-8477-735-2

9. Throughout the week, the writer saw in her circumstances much to lament and complain about. Using the graphic organiser, write all these down as well as the justification and reasons she gives for them. The first one has been done to help you.

Problems	Justification	Reason
Detention	Ms Black's foul mood	Late for school

Level 3

10. Write a word or a short phrase to explain the meaning of the following words as they are used in the passage.

a. foul ____________________ (paragraph 1)

b. bad hair day ____________________ (paragraph 4)

c. casually ____________________ (paragraph 9)

d. grounded ____________________ (paragraph 12)

 ISBN-978-81-8477-735-2

Vocabulary

A. Rewrite the following sentences in modern English.

1. I know thee not. Who art thou?

____

2. Hence and trouble me no more!

____

3. Yon fellow hath but one eye.

____

4. 'Twas toward eventide and the sun was sinking in the sky.

____

B. From the four words or phrases in the right-hand column, choose the one that most precisely expresses the meaning of the archaic word or phrase in the left-hand column.

Archaic English	Meaning			
1. henceforth	lately	again and again	still	from now on
2. hard by	around	far from	close to	inside
3. prithee	thank you	congratulations	my pleasure	please

 ISBN-978-81-8477-735-2

4. a score	ten	twenty	fifty	one hundred
5. yuletide	summer	rainy season	Christmas	high tide

C. Each of the following pairs of passages contains one example of direct characterisation (DC) and one example of indirect characterisation (IC). Write **DC** or **IC** against each of them.

1. (a) Robert is the sort of person who cannot throw anything away. He keeps the newspaper after he has read it each day in case he wants to read it again in a week's, a month's or possibly ten years' time. (   )

   (b) Robert finished the newspaper, folded it neatly, tucked it under his arm, walked thoughtfully along the passage and up the stairs to the second spare bedroom, where he carefully placed it on top of a pile of previous issues of the newspaper that was already over halfway to the ceiling. An article in today's paper had reminded him of something he had read in the same newspaper a few years ago. He wondered if he had time to go into the first spare bedroom and search for it. (   )

 ISBN-978-81-8477-735-2

2. (a) "Have you heard the latest about Rajiv?"
"He wasn't late again, was he?"
"He was five hours late. I mean five whole hours! How do you manage that? It'd take far less effort to get to places on time!" ( )

(b) Rajiv seemed to be by nature incapable of getting anywhere on time. He sometimes amazed his friends by what seemed like extraordinary feats of lateness. ( )

3. (a) My heart was going like a drum. I told myself the same thing that I always told myself. "Move with the crowd, keep your eyes on the person in front of you. If there's nobody in front of you, keep your eyes on the steps. Don't look up, don't look right, don't look left. It's only a footbridge at a railway station. You will get over it." ( )

(b) Julia was terribly scared of heights. Even something as safe and simple as crossing a footbridge at a railway station could be a source of terrible agitation for her. ( )

4. (a) Anish loved art. He wanted to surround himself with choice works by older and modern masters in elegant frames. Unfortunately, he was too poor to be able to indulge his passion in this way. He had to make do with what he could afford. ( )

(b) The walls of Anish's tiny room were covered in postcards, pages from newspapers and magazines, posters, cheap prints, faded engravings, which were fastened with small

 ISBN-978-81-8477-735-2

nails or drawing pins, stuck on with sticky tape, inserted into ill-fitting frames bought from a charity shop, propped up on any surface, sometimes overlapping one another as if they were plants in an overgrown garden competing for the light. When Anish lay in his narrow bed, he could look around and drink in art, art, nothing but art, and forget how lumpy the mattress was, and that in ten minutes or so he would have to get up and go to work in the hotel kitchen. (   )

D. Three characters take part in the following passage of dialogue. A is anxious and nervous; B is practical and sensible; C is vague and doesn't know what A and B are talking about. Write **A**, **B** or **C** in the blanks depending on which character you think is most likely to have said those particular words. The first one has been done to help you.

A : I've lost my purse, I've lost my purse! What am I going to do?

___: Keep calm. When did you last have it?

___: I can't remember. Did I pay for something this morning?

___: Hi!

___: Have you seen a purse anywhere?

___: It's pink. It's got all my money in it.

___: Sorry, what's that you're saying?

___: Why don't you switch off your I-player and listen?

___: Sorry, I've got my I-player on. That's better.

 ISBN-978-81-8477-735-2

___: I've lost all my money.

___: Have you seen a purse anywhere?

___: I don't think so ... unless it was a pink one.

___: Yes, yes, that's mine.

___: I think, I did see a pink purse somewhere but I can't remember where.

Grammar

A. Reconstruct the following sentences so that they become two clauses separated by a semicolon. Leave out any word, such as "and" or "but", and any punctuation marks that are no longer needed.

For example:
Mary came in a car but Lucy came on her bike.
Mary came in a car; Lucy came on her bike.

1. The dog is asleep by the fire and the cat is asleep in the dog's basket.

____

2. Once this house was surrounded by fields, but now it is in the middle of the city.

____

3. Jane was wearing a plain brown dress, while Peter wore red trousers and a yellow jacket.

____

 ISBN-978-81-8477-735-2

4. Tomorrow is the start of the school holiday, so the weather is bound to get worse.

____

5. Gordon doesn't know what is going on, and neither do the rest of us.

____

B. Match each verb and adverb pair in the left-hand column with a verb in the right-hand column that has the same meaning.

1.	shout loudly	loathe
2.	fall very fast	bellow
3.	hold tightly	batter
4.	dislike very much	plunge
5.	say softly	clasp
6.	hit repeatedly	whisper

C. Fill in each blank with the most appropriate verb.

1. Liquid was ____________ continuously from a small leak inside the washing machine and had already formed a large puddle on the floor.

- gushing
- trickling
- streaming
- oozing

 ISBN-978-81-8477-735-2

2. We had enough strength left for one last effort. Perhaps if we all _____________ on the rope together, we might be able to drag the vehicle clear of the mud.

- strained
- tugged
- jerked
- heaved

3. We wondered if we had come to the right place. There was no visible sign that people had ever lived here. All traces of human activity and human habitation had been _____________.

- disappeared
- removed
- obliterated
- ruined

4. The passageway that leads to the inner cave is so small that you have to _____________ through it on your hands and knees, keeping your head well down.

- kneel
- slither
- crouch
- crawl

Writing

A. Imagine that you are the girl's father in *Diary of a Teenage Girl*. Write a diary entry on the day Ms Jackson informs you of your daughter's detentions. You should keep your ideas largely based on the given text.

____

____

 ISBN-978-81-8477-735-2

B. Write a diary entry from the perspective of a teenager highlighting the stress and strain peculiar to your society. Ensure that your language and context have local flavour.

3 Sports

Comprehension

Read the passage.

Playing Politics in Sports

1 The decision of the English cricket team not to travel to Zimbabwe to take part in a World Cup fixture there in 2003 caused great controversy. There were those who argued that politics should be kept out of sport and that the match should go ahead. Others argued that the team should not go because to do so would be to give support to the oppressive regime there. Although the reason many of the players were reluctant to go to Harare was that their safety could not be guaranteed. There was even talk of death threats having been received.

2 The debate as to whether politics and sport should be kept apart is a long-running one. Yet history has shown not only that it is virtually impossible to keep these two apart, but also that major international sports events are often used as arenas to make major political statements of some kind.

3 South Africa's policy of apartheid was much condemned by many other nations and this condemnation was several times made evident at international sports events. South Africa was banned from taking part in the 1960 Olympic Games because of this policy. At the 1976 Olympic Games, held in Montreal, 22 African nations decided to boycott the Games because of the decision made not to bar New Zealand from taking part following its rugby team's tour of South Africa. At the 1986 Commonwealth Games, held in Edinburgh, 32 countries pulled out in protest at Britain's refusal to impose sanctions on South Africa.

4 The Olympic Games is no stranger to political sentiment. The 1968 Olympics, held in Mexico City, was used by some of the African - American athletes to draw attention to widespread grievances about racial injustice in the United States. Two of the athletes, Tommie Smith and John Carlos, who had won

 ISBN-978-81-8477-735-2

gold and bronze medals respectively in the 200 metres, stood on the winners' podium and raised their black-gloved fists over their heads as the American national anthem was played. This was known as the black power salute, the black power movement being the militant wing of the civil rights movement in the USA, which sought to end the disparity between the status of whites and blacks. The salute was a powerful, impressive indication to the rest of the world of how black people in America were feeling. The performance of the African American athletes was also powerful and impressive, since they won ten gold medals in the track and field events alone.

5 The 1972 Olympic Games, held in Munich, also became embroiled in political protest, and this time, the protest was both violent and bloody. On September 5, eight Arab terrorists stormed the Olympic village, killing two Israeli athletes and seizing nine more as hostages. They demanded the release of over 200 Palestinians who were serving prison sentences in Israeli jails along with two well-known German terrorists. Attempts to negotiate with the terrorists proved unsuccessful and they left for Munich's military airport with the hostages to get a flight back to the Middle East. At the airport, a terrible gun battle followed the killing of three of the Palestinians by German police marksmen. All nine of the hostages were killed in the shooting, as were two of the terrorists and a policeman.

6 The year 1972 was the first time the Olympics had been staged in Germany since 1936 when they were held in Berlin. On that occasion, Adolf Hitler, the Nazi leader, had two aims regarding the Games. He wished to use them both to make a political statement by emphasising his growing political power, and to make a racial statement by demonstrating the superiority of the Aryan race on the sports field. In his second aim, he was spectacularly unsuccessful because a black American athlete, Jesse Owens, won four gold medals. Hitler was furious and left the stadium without congratulating the athlete.

7 The Munich tragedy was the bloodiest of the Olympic political protests, but it was not the last of them. In 1980, the Moscow Olympics were boycotted by the USA, West Germany and Japan because of the Soviet invasion of Afghanistan, while four years later, the Soviet bloc of countries boycotted the Los Angeles Olympic Games in a retaliatory gesture.

 ISBN-978-81-8477-735-2

8 There is growing interest in international sports events with more and more nations participating, and more and more nations making a bid to host these important international occasions. These events should, ideally, be occasions of friendly rivalry which adds to international understanding. Alas, the international publicity, which such sports events attract, often lures people who have a political axe to grind, to use the events to bring attention to their political views or grievances. We have certainly not succeeded in keeping sports and politics in separate compartments.

A. Answer the following questions.

Level 1

1. Why did the English cricket players pull out of the 2003 World Cup fixture?

____

____

2. What did many countries do at past international events to register their protest against South Africa?

____

____

3. What was the political objective of the Arab terrorists who seized Israeli hostages from the Olympic village?

____

____

 ISBN-978-81-8477-735-2

4. What was the original goal of having an international sports event such as the Olympics?

____

____

Level 2

5. What was the intention of the two prize-winning African American athletes when they gave the black power salute?

____

____

6. In what ways were the Munich Games bloody and violent?

____

____

7. What was Hitler protesting against when he left the stadium without congratulating the black American athlete who had won four medals?

____

____

 ISBN-978-81-8477-735-2

8. Fill in the table with details to show how politics has intruded into the sports arena throughout history from 1936 to 2003.

Year	Event	Place	Countries involved	Political issue
1936				
1960				
1968				
1972				
1976				
1980				
1984				
1986				
2003				

 ISBN-978-81-8477-735-2

Level 3

9. Write a word or a short phrase to explain the meaning of the following words as they are used in the passage.

- long-running ______________________________ (paragraph 2)
- virtually ______________________________ (paragraph 2)
- sentiment ______________________________ (paragraph 4)
- disparity ______________________________ (paragraph 4)
- seizing ______________________________ (paragraph 5)

Vocabulary

A. Each of the words listed in the box has a special meaning in the vocabulary of a particular sport. Allocate each word to the appropriate sport.

bail	baseline	baton	birdie	boundary	goalkeeper
green	header	hole	hurdle	iron	lap
legside	lob	love	midfield	opener	over
par	pavilion	penalty	racquet	relay	service
smash	sprint	starting block	tee	throw-in	yellow card

athletics: ______________________________

cricket: ______________________________

football: ______________________________

golf: ______________________________

tennis: ______________________________

 ISBN-978-81-8477-735-2

B. The following nouns refer to people who are involved with sport, but are not actually players. Match each noun in the left-hand column with the correct description of what that person does from the right-hand column.

bookmaker/bookie	makes sure that the playing area is in a suitable condition for a contest
caddie	supervises a contest and makes sure that it is conducted fairly
groundsman	organises a sports event, especially a boxing match
promoter	carries a golfer's clubs
scorer	measures and records how long it takes an athlete to run a particular distance
sponsor	provides money to help a person or team
timekeeper	records how many points etc. each player or team has
umpire	takes bets on the result of a sporting contest, especially a horse race

C. The following sentences have to do with the different stages of a sporting competition. Select the correct answer for each blank.

1. Patel's victory over Chen in the quarter-final means that she will be playing Williams in the ____________.

- final
- play-off
- second round
- semi-final

 ISBN-978-81-8477-735-2

2. Jones's chances of reaching the final of the 400 metres must be reduced by the fact that three world-class athletes are running in her ______________.

- heat
- round
- race
- game

3. In order to ______________ for the finals of the World Cup, South Korea must come first or second in their group.

- enter
- qualify
- succeed
- pass

4. To everyone's surprise, last year's champion was ______________ in the first round.

- extirpated
- ousted
- eliminated
- discharged

5. Each of the four ______________ has defeated six other contestants to reach the last round of the competition.

- entrants
- finalists
- leaders
- losers

D. Match the sporting terms in the left-hand column with the appropriate definition from the right-hand column.

1.	chip	gentle shot that goes up in the air over another player or obstacle
2.	draw	goal or point that makes your score level with your opponent's

 ISBN-978-81-8477-735-2

3.	drive	an additional contest between two contestants whose scores are level at the end of the game
4.	equaliser	a game or contest that ends with the scores level
5.	play-off	a player who replaces another player during a game
6.	substitute	a powerful shot

E. Fill in the blanks with the appropriate words from the box.

seat	stand	ticket	met	fans
ground	play	warm up	applause	atmosphere

Philip hates to miss a single moment of any event that he has paid good money to go and see. When, for example, he has a ______________ to watch England play India at cricket at Lord's, he will make sure that he arrives at the ______________ even before the gates open. He chooses his ______________ with care. He wants the best view of the game that he can afford. If you too arrive early, you may find him sitting in the ______________ to the right of the pavilion. He will probably be discussing the prospects for the day's ______________ with other ______________ who are as knowledgeable as himself. They will watch the teams ______________ out on the field. They will drink in the ______________ as the stadium fills with spectators. They will discuss statistics and averages, and reminisce about previous occasions on which the two teams ______________. As they join in the ______________ that greets the umpires emerging from the pavilion, they may even feel that they have almost had their money's worth before a single ball has been bowled!

 ISBN-978-81-8477-735-2

Grammar

A. On the basis of their main meaning, sort the following adverbs into three categories: adverbs of manner, adverbs of time and adverbs of place.

abroad	abruptly	ago	around	beforehand
distinctly	downright	downstream	farther	heartily
henceforward	here	incessantly	lately	locally
momentarily	mysteriously	northward	notoriously	nowhere
preconsciously	presently	previously	recently	shortly
then	upstairs	vertically	virtuously	worldwide

Adverbs of manner	Adverbs of time	Adverbs of place

B. Select the adverbial phrase in each sentence that enables you to answer the following question.

For example:

Sonia was sitting quietly outside in the shade of a tree during her lunch break, when the fire alarm went off in the building next door.

Q: When did the fire alarm go off?

A: During Sonia's lunch break.

 ISBN-978-81-8477-735-2

1. Shortly before midnight, a large black car drew smoothly up outside the front entrance of the Excelsior Hotel.

Q: When did the car arrive?

A: ____________________

2. Sandra, already ten minutes late and still at home waiting for her taxi to arrive, was trying to button her coat with one hand, while holding her mobile phone in the other and speaking heatedly to her husband.

Q: How was Sandra buttoning her coat?

A: ____________________

3. I was standing impatiently at the bus stop in the rain at nine o'clock in the morning, when I suddenly remembered that I had an urgent appointment at ten past nine.

Q: Where was the speaker standing?

A: ____________________

4. By some unlucky chance, the handle of my shopping bag broke just as I was about to lift it into the back of the car, scattering shopping all over the car park.

Q: How did the handle of the bag break?

A: ____________________

5. At last, just when I was about to give up hope, I found my precious pocket knife inside one of my shoes at the very back of my wardrobe.

Q: Where was the missing pocket knife?

A: ____________________

 ISBN-978-81-8477-735-2

C. Pick out the adverbs and adverbial phrases of time, manner and place from the following passage. List them under the correct headings.

From her favourite armchair, Lucy watched intently as the runners began the final lap. She desperately wanted the Brazilian runner to win. He was not only very handsome, but his kit was yellow and blue. Yellow and blue had always been Lucy's favourite colours. There was no runner from Lucy's own country in the final.

For most of the race, the Brazilian had been in fourth or fifth position. He was running very sensibly, Lucy told herself. He was keeping some energy in reserve. He would need it during the final seconds of the race. The leading runners had already completed the back straight and were coming around the final bend. The Brazilian had moved into an outside lane. He had overtaken one runner. He was close behind another. He was just about to ...

The television set gave a crackle. The picture on the screen broke up into little coloured squares, then went blank. Lucy squealed with anguish. She was going to miss the finish.

Adverbs/Adverbials of time	Adverbs/Adverbials of manner	Adverbs/Adverbials of place

D. The sentences below need to be improved. Rewrite them by removing one definite or one indefinite article from each of them.

1. The teacher showed the great determination in bringing the class up to the required standard.

2. I'm giving you an official warning. The unsatisfactory work will no longer be tolerated by the management.

3. What a luck! I've been searching the bookshops for a book by this author and now I've found one on a market stall.

4. I've a feeling that Jim might find happiness at last with the girl that he met at the gym.

 ISBN-978-81-8477-735-2

5. He hasn't been seen for the weeks. The police have been searching the woods for him.

Writing

A. Research the Olympic Games over the years and write an article to show that the original goal of promoting friendship and understanding has been fulfilled.

 ISBN-978-81-8477-735-2

B. Choose one of the following Olympic episodes which have already been mentioned in the text. Find out more about it and write a short informative text that shows the ugly side of international sporting events.

1. The 1972 Munich Games
2. The 1936 Berlin Games

 ISBN-978-81-8477-735-2

4 Our Views

Comprehension

Read the passage.

School Uniform – The Pros and Cons

1 Most younger children do not mind wearing school uniform. Indeed, when they first start school, many of them are quite proud to wear it, regarding it as part of the exciting process of moving into a more grown-up world. Often, they plead to be able to wear their school uniform several times before they actually start school so that they can admire themselves in the mirror.

2 When they get older, their attitude often changes. Many pupils, particularly in secondary school, begin to object to the wearing of school uniform and question the necessity of it. So what are the pros and cons of having all the members of one school looking the same?

3 Those who oppose wearing of school uniform feel that it prevents pupils from expressing their individuality. Most of us express our personality through our choice of clothes, so why not school pupils? Opponents of school uniform feel that imposing a uniform style and colour of clothing is suppressing both the pupils' personality and individuality.

4 People who hold this point of view also feel that the practice of having all pupils wearing a uniform emphasises the institutional aspect of school. To them, it suggests that school, like prison, is rather an unpleasant place where they have to conform. Instead of presenting this bleak image of school, they feel that we should be encouraging children to regard school as a place where they will be allowed freedom of expression, and so a place where they want to be.

5 People on the other side of the fence of this debate, however, feel that all pupils wearing more or less identical clothing creates a sense of unity in the school. They feel that school uniform helps to create a team spirit in

 ISBN-978-81-8477-735-2

the same way that football colours do. Also, they feel that a school uniform inspires the same sense of pride and loyalty that football colours do.

6 Finally, supporters of school uniform point to a socio-economic advantage. If pupils are allowed to dress as they please, the poorer pupils will be set apart in an obvious way from their wealthier counterparts. On the other hand, if everyone is wearing the same style and colour of clothes, variations in quality of clothing are not all that obvious.

7 In the absence of school uniform, well-off pupils will be wearing quality clothes, or even designer clothes, and may well compete with each other to see whose clothes are the most fashionable and expensive. On the other hand, poorer pupils will be wearing what they can afford. Sometimes, this will mean very cheap, or even second-hand clothes and they will stand out like a sore thumb from their wealthier fellow pupils.

8 These, then, are the issues, which are relevant to the school uniform debate. I cannot help feeling that most parents will find it simpler and cheaper to opt for school uniform rather than allow their children to follow their fashion preferences.

A. Answer the following questions.

Level 1

1. What is the difference in attitude between younger and older children on the issue of wearing uniform?

___

___

2. To the opponents of school uniform, what would school be like if the uniform was used and what should school ideally be like?

___

___

 ISBN-978-81-8477-735-2

3. Which two groups of pupils are compared in the socio-economic argument in the school uniform debate?

____

____

4. According to the writer, what would the stand of parents be in the school uniform debate and why?

____

____

Level 2

5. Explain carefully how wearing school uniform suppresses both personality and individuality.

____

____

6. How does the example on football illustrate the sense in wearing uniform?

____

____

7. Explain in your own words the socio-economic argument for wearing uniform.

____

____

 ISBN-978-81-8477-735-2

8. Organise the arguments for and against wearing uniform in the table below.

Wearing uniform	
For	Against

Level 3

9. Write a word or a short phrase to explain the meaning of the following words as they are used in the passage.

a. plead ______________________ (paragraph 1)

b. imposing ______________________ (paragraph 3)

c. suppressing ______________________ (paragraph 3)

d. bleak ______________________ (paragraph 4)

e. variations ______________________ (paragraph 6)

 ISBN-978-81-8477-735-2

Vocabulary

A. Underline the examples of alliteration or assonance in the following sentences. Remember that alliteration and assonance depend on the sound of a word, not on the way in which it is written.

1. Look where Luke has put his foot.
2. Ravi wrote reams of rather rotten rhymes.
3. Sarah read the letter, then went to bed.
4. Simon lies beside his wife in the silent village churchyard.
5. Cynthia served sausages with a spicy curry sauce.

B. Construct an advertising slogan from the words given to you below, adding any other suitable word that you can think of. Use as much alliteration and assonance as possible.

For example:
crackers – crisp, crunchy
Christopher's crackers – created to be crisp and incredibly crunchy!

1. vacuum cleaner – devours dirt
2. tourist resort – happy holidays
3. cool or health drink – rapidly refreshing
4. sports car – fast, fashionable

 ISBN-978-81-8477-735-2

C. The following examples are written in a rather formal style. Rewrite them in a more informal style.

For example:
Be so kind as to close the door after you enter.
Please shut the door when you come in.

1. Prior to accepting a position with Chatterjee Ltd, Ahmed had been employed by Cohen and Cohen.

___

2. Please accept my sincere gratitude for your delightful gift.

___

3. Are you able to direct me to the railway station?

___

4. May I be of assistance? You seem to be unsure of your way.

___

5. I believe that this book may belong to you.

___

 ISBN-978-81-8477-735-2

D. Spoken English is, generally speaking, more informal than written English. Here is a passage of dialogue between two characters **A** and **B**. The words that **A** and **B** speak are shown below, but they are not in order. Your task is to reorder the lines of the dialogue by numbering them, so that they form a sensible conversation. The opening and closing sentences of the dialogue have been numbered for your convenience.

<u>1</u> **A:** Have you seen anything of Brian recently? Is he OK?

___ **B:** That doesn't sound like Brian. He's a pretty nice guy usually.

___ **A:** He used to. We've had a bit of a fall out.

___ **B:** And was your friend upset?

___ **A:** Well, he wasn't very nice to her.

___ **B:** Oh. That's news to me. What was that about?

___ **A:** Of course she was upset! So I was cross with Brian and haven't spoken to him since.

___ **B:** I'm sorry to hear that. What did he do to her exactly?

___ **A:** He was going out with a friend of mine. He didn't treat her very well.

___ **B:** I think so. You know him better than me.

___ **A:** He promised he'd take her to a party but he took someone else.

<u>12</u> **B:** Well, the last time I saw him, which was about a week ago, he looked OK.

E. Insert the words and phrases from the box into the correct spaces left in the following passage:

exactly	a hand	love	do with	that	a lot
cool	more	mind	reckons	pretty	anything

 ISBN-978-81-8477-735-2

"Have you seen Rajiv's new car?"

"No, what is it? He always said he wanted a sports car. Is it a sports car?"

"Not ______________. It's black."

"Black's a ______________ colour. But not a sports car?"

"He ______________ he can get 140k out of it if he works on the engine."

"That's ______________ good. How much work?"

"Quite ______________. Do you know ______________ about engines?"

"This and ______________. Does he need ______________?"

"He could probably ______________ some help, if you've got time."

"I'd ______________ to work on a sports car."

"Well, it's ______________ the sort of car you could go to watch sport in."

"Oh! Oh well, never ______________. Rajiv's a nice guy. I'll help him."

Grammar

A. Select the correct suffix from the box to form an adjective from each of the noun or verb roots listed. Remember that in some cases you may have to alter the root noun or verb slightly before you can attach the suffix.

For example:
glamour → glam<u>orous</u>
democracy → democra<u>tic</u>

-able	-al	-ful	-ic	-ical	-ly	-ous	-y

1. health ______________
2. beast ______________
3. humour ______________
4. mechanism ______________
5. anarchy ______________
6. terminus ______________

 ISBN-978-81-8477-735-2

7. eat ____________ 10. colour ____________

8. monster ____________ 11. tyranny ____________

9. realism ____________ 12. mud ____________

B. Many words in English, including many adjectives, are formed from words taken from Latin. In the table below, you will find a Latin word with its English meaning in the left-hand column and a brief definition of an adjective derived from it in the next one. Fill in the last column with the appropriate adjective. The first one has been done for you.

Word	Meaning	Adjective
1. *tempus* / ***tempor****is* (time)	lasting only a short time	**temporary**
2. ***signific****are* (to indicate, mean)	important	
3. ***host****is* (enemy, stranger)	unfriendly	
4. ***amic****us* (friend)	friendly	
5. ***vis****us* (sight)	relating to seeing or sight	
6. ***ard****ere* (to burn)	very enthusiastic, passionate	

 ISBN-978-81-8477-735-2

C. Divide the following list of adjectives into two groups – one that can only form their comparative and superlative using *more* and *most*, and the other that usually form them by adding -*er* and -*est*.

ancient	brown	brawny	comic	cutting	deadly	dreadful
great	horrible	incredible	jolly	lax	majestic	minute
naughty	onerous	reckless	tiny	varied	wicked	

Comparatives and superlatives using *more* and *most*	Comparatives and superlatives using -*er* and -*est*

D. Convert the sentences below in accordance with the instruction given in each case.

For example:
Tom is already as tall as his sister. (comparative)
Tom is already taller than his sister.

Tom is taller than any other boy in his class. (superlative)
Tom is the tallest boy in his class.

1. Sumita knows as much as most girls who are twice her age. (comparative)

 ISBN-978-81-8477-735-2

2. Their living room is as spacious as ours. (comparative)

____

3. Ravi is a better actor than anyone else in his family. (superlative)

____

4. This hotel is worse than any other I have ever stayed in. (superlative)

____

5. Paul used to be more generous than any other person I knew. (superlative)

____

6. Arundhati is as friendly as her sister. (comparative)

____

7. Uma is not as talented as her friend Samira. (comparative)

____

8. I like this necklace less than any of the others. (superlative)

____

 ISBN-978-81-8477-735-2

Writing

A. List your arguments for and against school uniform in the table below. Then present your arguments as an expository text. Remember to take a stand to say whether you are for or against wearing school uniform.

Wearing uniform	
For	Against

 ISBN-978-81-8477-735-2

B. Write an expository text on one of the topics below.

1. Teenagers are under too much pressure.
2. Homework is a waste of time.

5 Relations

Comprehension

Read the passage.

A Tribute to Grandma

1 To the world, Lucy Harris was a talented writer of highly successful crime novels. To me, she was my much-loved grandmother. In this second role she was really called Martha Jenkins, but had taken the *nom de plume* of Lucy Harris when her first novel was accepted for publication. When I asked her why she had chosen that particular name, she said that she had always liked the name Lucy, thinking it much more gentle and *mellifluous* than the rather harsh Martha. Harris she had chosen because she had visited the Scottish island of the same name with her parents as a girl and had fallen in love there for the first time. Who the young man was, she did not say. I wish I had thought of asking her.

2 I spent quite a long time at my grandmother's house when I was a little girl, partly because it was an oasis of peace compared with my parents' house which was only a short distance away. My parents were wonderful people and they adored each other and me, but they were both extremely volatile, argumentative people and could turn even the most clear-cut innocuous subject into a controversy. The slightest remark could spark off a heated debate. I frequently interpreted such a debate as a quarrel and took refuge in the calm of my grandmother's house.

3 It has to be said that my grandmother was not an especially calm person. She was, after all, the mother of my volatile mother and they were, in many ways, quite alike in temperament. When her work was going badly, she would pace up and down her study, exclaiming that she would never write again and smoking like a chimney. Although she was quite well aware of the health hazards of tobacco, she claimed that it was quite impossible for her to contemplate quitting smoking. She was convinced that if she stopped smoking, her muse would desert her.

 ISBN-978-81-8477-735-2

4 What made my grandmother's house a peaceful place was the presence of Mrs Burton. By the time she had published her fourth novel, my grandmother was extremely successful as a writer. Her books sold well in America and were translated into several languages. Her success brought with it a degree of wealth and, although my grandmother never cared a jot about money, it allowed her to employ a housekeeper, the redoubtable Mrs Burton.

5 I say redoubtable because most people regarded her in such a light. She acted as a kind of Cerberus to many people who tried to contact my grandmother, whether these were journalists seeking interviews or charities seeking money. Looking back, I realise that she was as much a personal assistant as a housekeeper, although typing was not among her many skills. Incidentally, my grandmother did not type and refused to employ a secretary. She insisted on writing her manuscripts in longhand and on sending them to her publishers in that condition. Her handwriting was far from copperplate, but, for years, she had a long-suffering editor who could interpret it.

6 Returning to Mrs Burton, I should say that she was only fierce with would-be interrupters. She knew that her employer was a disciplined writer, who wrote for three hours in the morning and three hours in the afternoon, stopping in the middle for a quick snack lunch. Mrs Burton would allow only the most dire of emergencies to interrupt this schedule.

7 Otherwise, she was charm itself. She was particularly charming and kind to me, although I must have been a bit of a nuisance. She worshipped my grandmother and did everything possible to make her life as comfortable and pleasant as possible. Without Mrs Burton, my grandmother would have been a less prolific writer.

8 During my visits to my grandmother's house, I did not spend all my time with Mrs Burton. My grandmother was an early bird, and even though she worked religiously for six hours a day, she was always free by the middle of the afternoon. Then we did all manner of things that children love. She pushed me on the swing which she had installed in the garden, she took me to feed the ducks on the village pond, we went on picnics together in the meadows behind her house, and we made frequent visits to the village shop to buy ice cream. Best of all, she told me stories.

 ISBN-978-81-8477-735-2

9 She sometimes read from books, but, more often, she made the stories up and these were much better than those in books. They were totally riveting and I often think what a wonderful children's writer she would have made. I gathered that this was suggested to her, but she always refused to deviate from her whodunnits. She had found a winning formula and was determined to stick to it. Who can blame her?

A. Answer the following questions.

Level 1

1. What explanation did Martha Jenkins give for her choice of the *nom de plume* "Lucy Harris"?

____

____

2. Who was Mrs Burton?

____

____

3. What activities did the writer and her grandmother enjoy together?

____

____

4. In your own words, explain what type of writing the writer's grandmother was particularly skilful at.

____

____

 ISBN-978-81-8477-735-2

Level 2

5. Why did the writer spend quite a long time at her grandmother's house when she was a little girl?

____

____

6. Why was it "impossible" for the writer's grandmother to stop smoking?

____

____

7. What did the writer mean by "Her handwriting was far from copperplate, but, for years, she had a long-suffering editor who could interpret it"?

____

____

8. "Mrs Burton turned out to be more than a housekeeper. She was also like a personal assistant to the writer's grandmother." In your own words, make a list of the duties covered by Mrs Burton as mentioned in or inferred from the passage.

____

____

 ISBN-978-81-8477-735-2

Level 3

9. Write a word or a short phrase to explain the meaning of the following words as they are used in the passage.

   a. innocuous ______________________________ (paragraph 2)

   b. contemplate ______________________________ (paragraph 3)

   c. dire ______________________________ (paragraph 6)

   d. prolific ______________________________ (paragraph 7)

   e. riveting ______________________________ (paragraph 9)

Vocabulary

A. The words in the left-hand column are commonly used in English to represent certain sounds. Match each of these words with the correct definition in the right-hand column.

Word	Definition
1. boo hoo	the sound of a dog barking
2. clip clop	the sound of a door knocker
3. ding dong	the sound of a person crying
4. rat-a-tat-tat	the sound of a horse's hooves
5. thud	the sound of a small bell
6. ting-a-ling	the sound of a large bell
7. woof woof	the sound made by a heavy object hitting something

 ISBN-978-81-8477-735-2

B. Fill in the blanks with words from the box.

sucking	pattering	hissing	beating	creaking
splashing	tinkling	bang	snorting	squelching

________________! The starter's pistol sounded for the start of the school's traditional cross-country race. It was not a nice day for a race. Rain was ________________ on the spectators' umbrellas as the runners left the school grounds by the bottom gate that led into a soggy field. The leaders were already ________________ through thick mud along the side of the field, watched by curious cattle who were ________________ and sending out puffs of steamy breath. The gate at the far end of the field was ________________ incessantly as runner after runner passed through before trying to tackle a short uphill path through some woods. Here, the mud was even thicker and stickier than it was in the field. As the runners put their feet down, the mud drew them in with a horrible ________________ sound. Several running shoes were lost in the quagmire – the unlucky contestants had to carry on in their socks or bare feet. For those who made it to the top of the hill, the going became slightly easier. The rain was still ________________ down, but when you are thoroughly wet already, you don't mind ________________ through a stream or two. Running back along wet pavement was a positive relief – except perhaps for those in bare feet. What kept them and everyone else going was the thought of hot water ________________ from a shower and the ________________ of spoons in mugs full of hot cocoa.

 ISBN-978-81-8477-735-2

C. You are a police officer investigating a burglary. The owner of the house has reported what happened and described the things that the thieves have taken. He thinks he has given a very helpful and detailed account. However, to you as a trained police officer, the report does not seem very helpful because it does not contain enough details. Write down the questions you would need to ask to try to obtain more useful details about the burglar and the crime.

Read the owner's report:

We heard a noise in the middle of the night. My wife heard it first. She woke me up and said, "I think I heard a noise."

"Do you mean downstairs?" I said, sleepily.

"Yes," she said. "Go and look."

I got out of bed and went downstairs very quietly and very carefully. My wife also came downstairs because she was too frightened to stay upstairs on her own if anyone was in the house.

We looked in the living room. There was nobody there. We looked in the dining room. There was someone in there.

It was not someone we knew. He was taking cutlery out of a box under the sideboard. My wife screamed very loudly. The man jumped out of the window before I could grab him and ran away.

We immediately called the police. While we were waiting for them to come, we looked to see what had been taken.

The man had been taking cutlery from a set that my wife's aunty had given us as a wedding present. It was a very beautiful set of cutlery and my wife was extremely fond of it. It will cost us a great deal of money to replace the pieces that have been taken.

The man had also taken my laptop computer that I had been using in the living room to do some extra work before I went to bed. He also took

 ISBN-978-81-8477-735-2

the DVD recorder that was under the television, but he did not take the TV itself because it has a 140 cm flat screen and is too big to carry.

He did not take anything from upstairs or from the kitchen.

I hope you will shortly catch the perpetrator of this dreadful crime.

Now, write your questions below:

____

____

____

____

____

____

____

D. You are the editor of a local newspaper. A very promising young reporter, Ramita Bose, has sent in an account of an incident that took place last night. Her writing is very vivid, but the account is too long. She has written well over 300 words. You only have space for a maximum of 250 words in the newspaper. Shorten the passage by omitting superfluous details. You may also make changes to the wording of the passage.

The residents of Tagore Lane were suddenly awoken by a bright flickering light in the middle of the night. When they drew their curtains and peeped out of their windows, they soon realised that a house in the middle of the street was on fire. Bright orange flames were leaping from its downstairs

 ISBN-978-81-8477-735-2

windows. The residents poured out of their houses. Word soon spread among the frightened residents that the fire service was on its way, but that people might be trapped on the upper floor. Would the fire service arrive in time to save them?

"We were worried that the firemen would arrive too late," said a neighbour, Mrs Bhuvana Chatterji, 42, mother of four. "It is very lucky that we have a hero living in Tagore Lane."

That hero is Mr Vijay Sen. Mr Sen came out of his house carrying a blanket soaked in water from his kitchen sink. Wrapping himself in this blanket, he unhesitatingly rushed into the neighbouring house without a thought for his own safety. After a few breathless seconds, he appeared at an upstairs window with a small child in his arms, Madhu Roy, aged two. He dropped Madhu into a blanket held by other neighbours, then fearlessly and uncomplainingly went back into the inferno and returned to the window a moment later with Madhu's elder sister, Sonia, aged four and a half. Sonia was also safely delivered to the blanket below.

By now, the whole house was ablaze and seemed about to collapse. Everyone feared for the life of Mr Sen and anyone else trapped inside the building. Luckily, the fire service arrived in the nick of time. Two fully equipped firefighters went in and brought out Mr Sen and the distraught mother of the two children, Mrs Ahalya Roy.

"It was only thanks to Mr Sen's bravery and heroism," said the chief fire officer Mr Tariq Bahadur later, "that a terrible human tragedy was prevented. I take my helmet off to him."

 ISBN-978-81-8477-735-2

Grammar

A. Insert the correct form of the infinitive (with or without "to") using the given verbs in brackets.

1. Robert wants ______________ Rebecca to the school dance. (take)
2. I need ______________ my hands before I have dinner. (wash)
3. I can barely ______________ what they are saying. (hear)

 ISBN-978-81-8477-735-2

4. I will _____________, but only if you're sure I won't be causing you any trouble. (stay)

5. In order _____________ this recipe, you will need 500 grams of minced lamb. (make)

6. It would be nice _____________ Julia again. (see)

B. Choose the correct form of the verb given at the end of each sentence to fill in the blank. You have to choose between three forms of the verb: the active infinitive (e.g. "to do"), the passive infinitive (e.g. "to be done") or the present participle (e.g. "doing"). If you put in an active or a passive infinitive, you must also decide whether it should be preceded by "to".

For example:
Everyone thinks that Jack is going _____________ as captain. (choose).
Everyone thinks that Jack is going <u>to be chosen</u> as captain.

1. I decided _____________ to work today. (walk)

2. We discussed whether _____________ Michael or not. (invite)

3. I hope _____________ for the school team. (pick)

4. I talked to Soraya about _____________ a picnic next weekend. (organise)

5. The job must _____________ by tomorrow afternoon, or you won't get paid. (finish)

6. I can't help _____________ that Sanjit knows more about this matter than he will admit. (think)

 ISBN-978-81-8477-735-2

C. The left-hand column lists the different tenses. The right-hand column contains different forms of the verb "move". Match each tense with the correct form of "move".

Tense	Forms of verb
1. present tense	she would have moved
2. future tense	they moved
3. simple past tense	we are moving
4. perfect tense	you will be moving
5. past perfect tense	I would move
6. conditional tense	he was moving
7. past conditional tense	she will move
8. present continuous tense	he had moved
9. future continuous tense	they move
10. past continuous tense	I have moved

D. Fill in each blank with the correct form of the verb in brackets.

For example:

School finished yesterday and now we ____________ in the garden. (play)

School finished yesterday and now we are playing in the garden.

1. As soon as Tom ____________ work, he rushed off to the tennis court. (finish)

 ISBN-978-81-8477-735-2

2. Lakshmi must finish this job before she ____________ another. (start)

3. I ____________ the fish yesterday, so it should still be quite fresh. (buy)

4. Don't interrupt your father while he ____________. (work)

5. I ____________, unless my mother's illness gets worse. (come)

6. Jane ____________ the film already, and she says it's very good. (see)

E. Rewrite this passage as if the events it describes took place at an earlier time. In other words, change all the verbs in the present tense into verbs in the past tense or present perfect tense and all the verbs in the present perfect tense into verbs in the past perfect tense, etc.

The opening of the passage is rewritten here as an example:

I want a pet very badly. I have never had a pet before. In fact, nobody in our family has had a pet before, as far as I know.

I wanted a pet very badly. I had never had a pet before. In fact, nobody in our family had had a pet before, as far as I knew.

Now, read and rewrite the passage.

I want a pet very badly. I have never had a pet before. In fact, nobody in our family has had a pet before, as far as I know. My elder brothers and sisters certainly have not. I don't think that they like animals very much. They definitely don't feel about animals the way I do – neither does my father. I think my mother may be more sympathetic, though. She says that little dogs and cats are very sweet. I hope she will let me have a pet one day. However, she also says that little dogs and cats grow into big dogs and cats that cost an awful lot to feed. Also, when you are not looking, they drop hairs on the carpet and bite the legs of the table. Personally, I think that growing up to be a big, strong healthy animal is a good thing

 ISBN-978-81-8477-735-2

and not a bad thing. And if our furniture is so precious, why does she let my big brothers bounce on the armchairs? In any case, I am not interested in having a dog or a cat. No, I want a mongoose. A mongoose will not drop hairs or chew the furniture, and it will also be very good for killing snakes.

Writing

A. In the style of the passage *A Tribute to Grandma*, write a biography of someone important to you. It could be your parent, teacher, friend or mentor.

 ISBN-978-81-8477-735-2

B. Write your autobiography in which you narrate and describe the highs and lows of your childhood.

 ISBN-978-81-8477-735-2

6 Technology

Comprehension

Read the passage.

Dolly the Sheep

1 It is by no means uncommon for animals to play a part in scientific research, but most of them remain anonymous, and none of them have achieved the international fame of Dolly the Sheep. Dolly owes her place in scientific history to the fact that she was the first animal to be cloned from an adult cell. Her birth took place on 5 July 1996 at the Roslin Institute near Edinburgh in Scotland and, when the birth was announced in February 1997, the world's press could not get there fast enough. Dolly was the most photographed sheep ever.

2 Dolly's arrival was not without humour. To start with, there was the fact that she was named after the large-breasted American country-and-western singer Dolly Parton, having been cloned from cells taken from the udder of an adult ewe. This was a source of much amusement to some of the press. Then, there was the fact that some people wondered if the announcement of her arrival was a hoax.

3 However, the cloning of Dolly was not a hoax. It had taken place and it was considered a very serious event indeed. Not only was her cloned birth a scientific breakthrough of tremendous importance, but it gave rise to much press and public debate about the social and ethical implications of the event.

4 Some accused the Roslin scientists, headed by Ian Wilmut, of playing God. Reproduction should be undertaken only by the usual sexual process and any other process was unthinkable. People seemed to forget that it was a sheep, and not a human, that had been cloned and there was much debate about what effect human cloning would have on the future of mankind.

 ISBN-978-81-8477-735-2

5 There was talk about future male involvement in reproduction becoming unnecessary and there was much scaremongering about evil people making several clones of themselves and adding to the miseries of the world. One German newspaper raised the possibility of a regiment of cloned Hitlers bringing destruction to the world. On a more harrowing note, some parents took false hope from the news of Dolly that they might somehow replicate children who were dying or even children who were dead.

6 One of the major problems was that people did not understand what had happened or why it had happened, and people fear the unknown. To be fair, it was difficult to get one's head round the fact that it was possible to create an animal that was an exact copy of, and had exactly the same genetic make-up of, another animal. Previously cloning, if not within the pages of a science fiction publication, had been thought of only in terms of the plant world.

7 What had actually happened was that the Roslin scientists had taken a cell from the udder of a six-year-old Finn Dorset ewe and coupled it with an unfertilised egg from a Blackface ewe, an electric current being used to encourage the fusion of the two. The artificially created embryo, which was the result of this fusion, was cultured for seven days in the lab and then transferred to the womb of another sheep, which then became pregnant.

8 The aspects of the birth of Dolly which most excited the scientific world was that she had been created from an adult cell. The Roslin Institute had already cloned two ewes, known as Megan and Morag, which were born in 1995, but they had been cloned from cultured embryo cells, not adult cells. The birth of Dolly proved that the cells in our bodies are much more versatile than they were previously thought to be. Pre Dolly, it had been assumed that all the cells in our bodies were rather fixed in their functions. The creation of Dolly suggested, as one of the scientists involved pointed out, that, for example, bone marrow cells might be used to help heal injuries to the heart, muscles or other parts of the body.

9 His example indicates the reason behind the research which led to the creation of Dolly. Dolly's birth was a part of research into cloning for therapeutic purposes. She was brought into being in an attempt to advance the treatment of disease in humans, not as a prelude to human cloning.

  ISBN-978-81-8477-735-2

10 Nevertheless, Dolly's birth sparked off a debate on the ethical issues connected with human cloning, and, indeed, to a lesser extent, with animal cloning, but there are other issues to be taken into consideration as well. Several scientists working in the field of animal cloning have warned against attempts at cloning humans because of such risks as foetal deformity and premature ageing or disease.

11 Dolly's premature death, which occurred in February 2003, when she was six years old as a result of a viral lung disease, brought more of these warnings. It was not clear whether her death, or the arthritis from which she had been suffering, had anything to do with the fact that she had been cloned, but it caused concern about cloning generally.

12 The talk of human cloning at the time of Dolly's birth was extremely premature. Even by the time Dolly's death was announced, no instance of human cloning had been proved to have taken place, although several claims relating to this had been made. I think that many of us would agree with the reported comments of Dr Harry Griffith of the Roslin Institute, "If a child was cloned that would go over a barrier that I don't think society should cross."

A. Answer the following questions.

Level 1

1. Describe the two reactions to the cloning of Dolly when the news first broke.

____

____

2. State one reason given in the passage that explains the social and ethical furore created by Dolly.

____

____

 ISBN-978-81-8477-735-2

3. What was the original purpose of the research that led to Dolly's creation? What was the research not intended for?

4. What was Dolly's health condition like at the time of her death?

Level 2

5. What does the writer cite as a frightful consequence with far-reaching effects if human cloning takes place?

6. What is the difference between the method by which Dolly was created and the conventional method of cloning?

 ISBN-978-81-8477-735-2

7. Fill in the table to show the social, ethical and medical implications of the Dolly event and the human cloning issue that followed.

Implications		
Social	Ethical	Medical

Level 3

8. Write a word or a short phrase to explain the meaning of the following words as they are used in the passage.

a. anonymous ______________________________ (paragraph 1)

b. implications ______________________________ (paragraph 3)

c. fusion ______________________________ (paragraph 7)

d. prelude ______________________________ (paragraph 9)

e. premature ______________________________ (paragraph 10)

 ISBN-978-81-8477-735-2

Vocabulary

A. Each word listed in the box relates to one of the three different areas of technology: aircraft and aviation; cars and motor vehicles; computers and computing. Write these words under the correct headings.

altimeter	byte	autopilot	bonnet
bumper	disc brake	clutch	cockpit
cookie	hard drive	drag	flaps
fuselage	pixel	indicator	radiator grille
memory stick	tablet	power steering	thrust
server	undercarriage	tailfin	webcam
wifi	automatic transmission	virus	internal-combustion engine
touch screen	wingspan		

Aircraft and aviation	Cars and motor vehicles	Computers and computing

 ISBN-978-81-8477-735-2

B. Many technical words in English have their origins in words from ancient Greek or Latin. Try to complete the following words using the short definition of the word itself and the explanation of its Greek or Latin root.

1. ____________pter (flying machine) (*pteron* means "wing" in Greek)

2. tele____________ (thing for seeing at a distance) (*tele* means "at a distance" in Greek)

3. holo____________ (a 3D image of something) (*holo* means "whole" in Greek)

4. ____________meter (a thing for measuring temperature) (*metrum* means "measure" in Greek)

5. ____________frig____________ (a thing for keeping food cold) (*frigus* means "cold" in Latin)

C. Match each word in the left-hand column with its correct antonym from the list in the right-hand column.

Word	Antonym
attack	despair
bend	contract
catch	meanness
courage	straighten
entrance	drop
expand	defend
generosity	exit
hit	miss
hope	cowardice

 ISBN-978-81-8477-735-2

D. Change each word in the list below into a word of the opposite meaning by altering the prefix.

Word	Antonym
1. encode	
2. exclude	
3. implode	
4. inhale	
5. optimistic	
6. prewar	

E. Rewrite the following sentences replacing as many of the words in them as you can with their antonyms.

Note: You may sometimes have to change the order of words or clauses in the sentence so that they make better sense.

For example:
Ravi sat down and switched the computer on.
Ravi switched the computer off and stood up.

1. Vijay beat Krishnan at tennis.

____

2. Mary arrived before Diana left.

____

 ISBN-978-81-8477-735-2

3. Samira dislikes coffee without milk.

____

4. The car turned left and headed off in an easterly direction.

____

5. Their spirits rose higher and higher, and they began to feel really elated.

____

6. David suddenly realised that the painting that he thought was worth a lot of money, was actually fake.

____

Grammar

A. Turn each of the following pairs of sentences into a single sentence containing a conditional clause that begins with the word or phrase given in brackets.

For example:
We shall have a picnic tomorrow. The weather must be fine. (provided that)
We shall have a picnic tomorrow provided that the weather is fine.

1. You can go. You must be home by ten o'clock. (on condition that)

____

2. There will be enough biscuits for everyone. People should only take one each. (if)

____

 ISBN-978-81-8477-735-2

3. You will be there by six o'clock. The traffic may make you late. (unless)

____

4. The car will start. There must be petrol in the tank. (provided that)

____

5. I don't care who else comes. What matters is that my best friend Peter is there. (so long as)

____

6. We will still go camping. It may rain or thunder. (even if)

____

B. Complete the following dialogue using the words and phrases in the box.

provided that	by the way	if necessary	if	likely
rather	depends	whether	possible	unless

A: Could you come in to work on Saturday, ______________?

B: Why, what's happening?

A: The boss is asking for volunteers. We might get a big order from Singapore that would have to be dealt with very quickly.

B: How ______________ are we to get it?

 ISBN-978-81-8477-735-2

A: It ____________________ on a number of factors, she says – mainly on ____________________ we offer a better deal than our competitors.

B: When will we know?

A: By tomorrow, ____________________ everything goes according to plan. Anyway, are you available?

B: It's ____________________ that I might be. In fact, I will be ____________________ I'm picked to play for the club team.

A: Which club team is that?

B: The cricket club. ____________________, would we be paid extra for working on a Saturday?

A: The boss hasn't said anything about that yet. But ____________________ she wants people to come in on Saturday, she'll have to make it worth their while, don't you think?

B: Perhaps. Still, given the chance, I'd ____________________ play cricket.

C. Without changing the meaning of the sentences below, replace the underlined part of each one with a shorter and simpler clause or sentence containing a modal verb:

For example:
I am going out now and <u>it is possible that I shall not be back until late tonight</u>.
I am going out now and I may not be back until late tonight.

 ISBN-978-81-8477-735-2

1. Am I allowed to go now or do I have to stay until the end?

____

2. Paul and Laura are out at the moment, but it is likely that they will be back by about nine o'clock.

____

3. It is compulsory for you to buy a ticket before you board the train.

____

4. It was so noisy in there that it was impossible for us to hear ourselves think.

____

5. Have you checked your voicemail? It is possible that Laura has left a message.

____

6. It is not possible for me to go with you to Australia, I do not have enough money.

____

D. Complete the following dialogue using the words in the box.

could	let's	need	should	may
won't	didn't	don't	might	must

Z: According to the instructions, part A __________ fit into part B – but it doesn't.

 ISBN-978-81-8477-735-2

Y: ______________ I look?

Z: Here are the instructions. Here's the plan.

Y: I see. Why ______________ it fit?

Z: I don't know. I ______________ make the chair. I'm only trying to put it together.

Y: All right. Calm down. ______________ you pass me my glasses, please?

Z: Here they are.

Y: Right, ______________ have a look. It definitely says that Part A fits into Part B.

Z: Yes.

Y: You ______________ have the wrong parts. Are you absolutely sure that this is Part A.

Z: It has Part A written on it. Look!

Y: ______________ get upset. If this is part A, it ______________ fit into part B.

Z: But it doesn't!!!

Y: I ______________ a little time to think about this.

Writing

A. Write an article for a school publication on the cloning of Dolly. In your article, you should include the following:

1. Details about the cloning, for example, where, when and why it happened
2. General reactions to the cloning
3. Your views about cloning

____

____

 ISBN-978-81-8477-735-2

B. Write an informative text on a recent medical or scientific breakthrough of your choice.

 ISBN-978-81-8477-735-2